Interactive Mathematics Program®

I M P ™

Integrated High School Mathematics

Solve It!

Dan Fendel and Diane Resek
with
Lynne Alper and Sherry Fraser

Key Curriculum Press
in Mathematics Education

D1366470

This material is based upon work supported by the National Science Foundation under award number ESI-9255262. Any opinions, findings, and conclusions or recommendations expressed in this publication are those of the authors and do not necessarily reflect the views of the National Science Foundation.

Key Curriculum Press
1150 65th Street
Emeryville, California 94608
email: editorial@keypress.com
http://www.keypress.com

10 9 8 7 6 5 4 3   05 04 03 02
ISBN 1-55953-464-8
Printed in the
United States of America

Project Editor
Casey FitzSimons

Editorial Assistant
Jeff Gammon

Production Editors
Caroline Ayres, Kristin Ferraioli

Art Developer
Jason Luz

Original Cover and Interior Design
Terry Lockman, Lumina Designworks

Art and Design Coordinator
Caroline Ayres

Production Managers
Steve Rogers, Luis Shein, Diana Jean Parks

Production Coordination
Diana Krevsky, Susan Parini, Laurel Roth Patton

Technical Graphics
Kristen Garneau, Natalie Hill, Greg Reeves

Illustration
Tom Fowler, Evangelia Philippidis, Sara Swan,
Diane Varner, Martha Weston, April Goodman Willy

Publisher
Steven Rasmussen

Editorial Director
John Bergez

MATHEMATICS REVIEW
Rick Marks, Ph.D., Sonoma State University,
    Rohnert Park, California

MULTICULTURAL REVIEWS
Mary Barnes, M.Sc., University of Melbourne,
    Cremorne, New South Wales, Australia
Edward D. Castillo, Ph.D., Sonoma State University,
    Rohnert Park, California
Joyla Gregory, B.A., College Preparatory School,
    Oakland, California
Genevieve Lau, Ph.D., Skyline College, San Bruno, California
Beatrice Lumpkin, M.S., Malcolm X College (retired),
    Chicago, Illinois
Arthur Ramirez, Ph.D., Sonoma State University,
    Rohnert Park, California

TEACHER REVIEWS
Daniel R. Bennett, Kualapuu, Hawaii
Larry Biggers, San Antonio, Texas
Dave Calhoun, Fresno, California
Dwight Fuller, Clovis, California
Daniel S. Johnson, Campbell, California
Brent McClain, Hillsboro, Oregon
Amy C. Roszak, Roseburg, Oregon
Carmen C. Rubino, Lakewood, Colorado
Jean Stilwell, Minneapolis, Minnesota
Wendy Tokumine, Honolulu, Hawaii

Contents

Solve It!

Days 13-21: What's the Same?

Days 22-26: The Linear World

Days 27-31: Beyond Linearity

Appendix: Supplemental Problems 91

Interactive Mathematics Program®

I M P

Integrated High School Mathematics

Solve It!

Days 1-5

Solving Equations and Understanding Situations

For many people, mathematics means solving equations. You will, in fact, solve lots of equations in this unit. But solving equations makes more sense if those equations describe something meaningful.

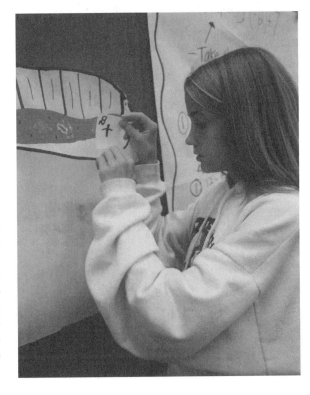

Tiffany Bock dramatically demonstrates to the class a model for understanding the arithmetic of positive and negative numbers.

After a look back at Year 1, this unit takes up the challenge of representing situations using algebra and equations. Some of the situations you will study may be familiar from Year 1. The opening days of this unit also include some review of the arithmetic of positive and negative numbers, in the context of a Year 1 Problem of the Week.

Start POWs Earlier

Be More Active in Class

Ask Questions

Complete Assignments

Homework 1 Math, Me, and the Future

1. Write about how your first year in IMP affected the way you think about mathematics.

2. Write about how the mathematics classes you had before IMP prepared you for Year 1 of IMP.

3. On a separate sheet of paper, write a letter to yourself. Set goals for yourself for the future, imagining that you are your own conscience. You can ask yourself some questions and give yourself some reminders about what you would like to do to succeed in mathematics as you continue in school.

Tomorrow in class you will put this letter in an envelope that you address to yourself. Your letter will be delivered to you some time in the future.

Memories of Yesteryear

In this assignment, you will be solving problems based on situations that may be familiar to you. Although you might prefer to solve some of the problems without equations, your assignment is to use variables and equations according to these steps.

- Choose the variable you are going to use in each problem and state what it represents.

- Write an equation, using your variable, that represents the problem.

- Solve the equation and the problem using any method you wish, including guess and check (also known as "trial and error").

1. From *Patterns*

   A chef put several batches of cubes into a cauldron. The first batch contained 27 cubes. The last batch contained 56 cubes. A total of 108 cubes were put into the cauldron.

   How many cubes did the chef throw in that were not part of the first or last batch?

2. From *The Overland Trail*

   Each adult needed 5 yards of shoelace for the trip to California and each child needed 3 yards. A certain family with seven children needed 71 yards of shoelace.

   How many adults were in the family?

Continued on next page

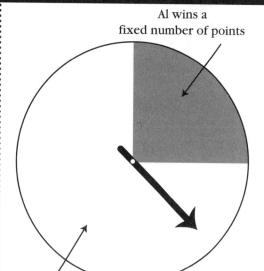

Al wins a
fixed number of points

Betty wins 2 points

3. From *The Game of Pig*

Al and Betty were playing a game using the spinner shown here. Betty won 2 points from Al every time the spinner landed on the white section.

Al won a fixed amount from Betty when the spinner landed in the gray section, but you don't know what that amount was. You do know that after 100 games, the results matched the probabilities perfectly, and Al was 25 points ahead of where he started.

How much did Al win from Betty each time the spinner landed in the gray section?

4. From *The Pit and the Pendulum*

A group was doing experiments in order to find the period of a pendulum in terms of its length. The group came up with this rule:

If you take the square root of the length of the pendulum (in inches) and multiply that by 0.32, then you will get the number of seconds for one period of the pendulum.

If the period of a certain pendulum is 3.84 seconds, then what is the pendulum's length (based on this rule)?

5. From *Shadows*

A person who is 6 feet tall is standing 3 feet from a small mirror that is lying flat on the ground. By looking in the mirror, the person can see the top of a tree that is 15 feet from the mirror.

How tall is the tree?

Homework 2   Building a Foundation

1. Maisha is planning to build a patio along the back wall of her house, which is 32 feet long. The patio will be rectangular in shape and will fit against the full length of the back wall (so one side of the patio will be 32 feet long).

   The patio will be built out of square tiles that are 1-foot-by-1-foot. Maisha is thinking about this question:

   > If I have 256 tiles to work with, how far out from the wall will the patio extend?

Pretend you are Maisha and do these tasks:

- Make a sketch of the situation.

- Choose the variable you are going to use and state what it represents.

- Write an equation that represents the problem.

- Solve the equation and the problem using any method you wish (including trial and error).

2. Benito is also going to build a patio, but his patio does not have to fit exactly against a wall. In fact, all that Benito has decided is that the patio should be rectangular in shape and should use all of the 144 tiles he has available. (Like Maisha, he is using square tiles that are 1-foot-by-1-foot.)

   Find as many possibilities as you can for the dimensions of Benito's patio. (*Note:* You do not need to go through all the steps you used in Question 1.)

Homework 3

You're the Storyteller

In *Memories of Yesteryear,* you started from situations and created equations to fit those situations. In this assignment, you will work in the opposite direction, creating situations that fit the five equations given here. This task has three steps.

• Create a situation.

• Write a question about the situation so that solving the equation will give you the answer to your question. State clearly what the variable in the equation represents in the situation.

• Solve the equation to answer your question.

1. $4a = 12$

2. $r + 5 = 20$

3. $2m + 1 = 11$

4. $\frac{t}{3} = 8$

5. $13 - f = 6$

Is It a Digit?

There are five empty boxes shown here labeled 0 through 4.

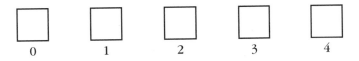

| | | | | |
| 0 | 1 | 2 | 3 | 4 |

Your task is to put a digit from 0 through 4 *inside* each of the boxes so that certain conditions hold:

• The digit you put in the box labeled "0" must be the same as the number of 0's you use.

• The digit you put in the box labeled "1" must be the same as the number of 1's you use.

• The digit you put in the box labeled "2" must be the same as the number of 2's you use, and so on.

Of course, you are allowed to use the same digit more than once.

You may want to make several copies of the set of boxes in order to try various combinations of digits.

What Not to Do

Here is an example of an *incorrect* way to fill in the boxes.

| 2 | 3 | 1 | 2 | 2 |
| 0 | 1 | 2 | 3 | 4 |

This is incorrect for many reasons. For instance, there is a 1 in the box labeled "2," but there is more than one 2 used in the boxes. Similarly, there is a 2 in the box labeled "4," but the number of 4's used is not equal to 2.

POW 1 *A Digital Proof*

0	1	2	3	4
□	□	□	□	□

In *Is It a Digit?* you looked for a way to fill in the numbered boxes shown here in a way that fit certain conditions. Your task in this POW is to *prove* that you have all the solutions. (If you haven't yet found a solution, then doing so is also part of your POW.)

Write-up

1. *Problem Statement:* Explain the problem from *Is It a Digit?*

2. *Process:* Based on your notes, describe how you went about finding all of the solutions to *Is It a Digit?* and how you decided that you had them all.

3. *Solutions:* List all solutions you found for *Is It a Digit?* Then write a careful and detailed proof that there are no solutions to *Is It a Digit?* other than those you listed.

4. *Evaluation*

5. *Self-assessment*

(For write-up categories with no specific instructions, use the description in *The Standard POW Write-up.*)

The Standard POW Write-up

Each POW is unique, and so the form of the write-up may vary from one POW to the next. Nevertheless, most of the categories that you will be using for your POW write-ups will be the same throughout the year.

The list below gives a summary of the standard categories for POW Write-ups.

Some POW write-ups will use other categories or require more specific information within a particular category in order to make the write-up more suitable to the POW. But if the write-up instructions for a given POW simply list a category by name, you should use the descriptions below.

Continued on next page

The Standard POW Write-up Categories

1. *Problem Statement:* State the problem in your own words. Your problem statement should be clear enough that someone unfamiliar with the problem could understand what it is that you are being asked to do.

2. *Process:* Describe what steps you took in attempting to solve this problem, using your notes to jog your memory. Include steps that didn't work out or that seemed like a waste of time. Complete this part of the write-up even if you didn't solve the problem. And if you got help of any kind on the problem, indicate what form it took and how it helped you.

3. *Solution:* State your solution as clearly as possible. Explain why you think your solution is correct and complete. (If you obtained only a partial solution, give that. If you were able to obtain more general results, include them.)

   Your explanation should be written in a way that will be convincing to someone else—even someone who initially disagrees with your answer.

4. *Evaluation:* Discuss your personal reaction to this problem. For example, you might comment on these questions.

   • Did you consider the problem educationally worthwhile? What did you learn from it?

   • How would you change the problem to improve it?

   • Did you enjoy working on the problem?

   • Was the problem too hard or too easy?

5. *Self-assessment:* Assign yourself a grade for your work on this POW, and explain why you think you deserve that grade.

Homework 4

Running on the Overland Trail

For each of the problems here, complete these tasks.

- Choose a variable.

- State clearly what the variable represents.

- Write an equation using your variable that represents the problem.

- Solve both the equation and the problem.

1. If Phillipe had $7 more, he could buy a $30 pair of tennis shoes. How much money does he have?

2. Yolanda jogged 2 miles to a lake, ran twice around the lake, and then jogged 2 more miles home. Altogether she traveled 10 miles. How far is it around the lake?

3. An Overland Trail family is carrying 5 gallons of water per person in its wagon. Unexpectedly, two stragglers join the group. The family figures out that this means there are now only 4 gallons per person. How many people were in this Overland Trail family?
   (*Hint:* Take a guess and write down what you should do to see if it's right. Keep doing this until you see a pattern in the arithmetic steps. Then use these steps to come up with an equation.)

Lamppost Shadows

Chantelle and Nelson are members of a volunteer clean-up committee. At the end of the day they are waiting with other volunteers for the shuttle back to the community center.

1. Chantelle is 5 feet tall. She is standing 30 feet from a lamppost that is 25 feet tall. Using S to stand for the length of Chantelle's shadow, you can represent her situation using the diagram shown here.

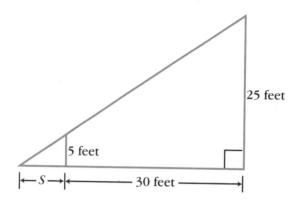

a. Take a guess as to how long the shadow is, *just from looking at the diagram*.

b. Explain, using the diagram, why S must fit the equation

$$\frac{S}{S + 30} = \frac{5}{25}$$

c. Try to find a number for S that solves this equation. If you can't solve the equation exactly, look for a number that comes close.

d. Compare your answer in Question 1c to your guess in Question 1a. Does your answer in Question 1c seem reasonable?

2. Nelson, who is 6 feet tall, is standing 20 feet from the same lamppost.

a. Draw and label a diagram showing Nelson and his shadow.

b. Write an equation whose solution would give the length of Nelson's shadow.

c. Try to find a number that solves your equation from Question 2b. If you can't solve the equation exactly, look for a number that comes close.

Homework 5

1-2-3-4 Puzzle with Negatives

This assignment is based on *POW 2: 1-2-3-4 Puzzle* from the Year 1 unit *Patterns*. The idea of that problem was to use the digits 1, 2, 3, and 4 once each, along with arithmetic operations, to create expressions with different numerical values. Such expressions are called **1-2-3-4 expressions.** For instance, $1 + (2 + 3) \cdot 4$ is a 1-2-3-4 expression for the number 21.

Unlike the original problem, this assignment involves negative as well as positive integers, so read the instructions carefully.

The Task

Create as many 1-2-3-4 expressions as you can for each of the numbers from –20 to 20, using the rules outlined here.

Continued on next page

The Rules

There is one essential rule for forming 1-2-3-4 expressions.

- You must use each of the digits 1, 2, 3, and 4 exactly once.

The digits can be combined using any of these methods.

- You may use any of the four basic arithmetic operations—addition, subtraction, multiplication, and division (according to the order-of-operations rules).

- You may use exponents.

- You may use radicals or factorials.

- You may juxtapose two or more digits to form a number such as 12.

- You may use parentheses and brackets to change the meaning of the expression.

- You may use a negative sign in front of any of the digits 1, 2, 3, or 4. For example, $-3 \cdot (4^2 - 1)$ is a 1-2-3-4 expression for the number -45. (This method was not included in the original problem.)

Note: You may *not* just put a negative sign in front of an entire expression. For example, $-(3 + 4! + 1 - 2)$ is *not* a legitimate 1-2-3-4 expression for -26, even though $-(3 + 4! + 1 - 2)$ is equal to -26 and uses each digit exactly once. You can only put the negative sign in front of an individual digit.

Days 6–12

Keeping Things Balanced

What is an equation? What does it mean to solve an equation? *Homework 6: The Mystery Bags Game* introduces a simple game using a pan balance that will be used throughout the unit as a way to think about these questions.

Over the next few days, you'll review ideas about substitution and order of operations. You'll work with families of algebraic expressions and use functions to represent situations.

For now, trial and error will be one of the main tools for solving equations, but you'll also begin using graphs and seeing how valuable a graphing calculator can be for solving equations.

Jeff Trubitte and Rafael Pozos created two different outcomes for "POW 2: Tying the Knots."

Homework 6

The Mystery Bags Game

Do you remember the king in the "Bags of Gold" POWs? Well, he doesn't let the gold out of his sight anymore. But it can get very boring watching gold all day, so he has the court jester make up games for him to pass the time.

The game the king loves best is the mystery bags game. First, the jester takes one or more empty bags and fills each bag with the same amount of gold. These bags of equal weight are called the "mystery bags." Next, the jester digs into his collection of lead weights. He takes out his pan balance and places some combination of mystery bags and lead weights on the two pans so that the two sides balance.

The game is to figure out the weight of each mystery bag.

Continued on next page

Your Task

The game may sound rather easy, but it can get very difficult for the king. See if *you* can win the mystery bags game in the various situations described here by figuring out how much gold there is in each mystery bag.

Explain how you know you are correct. You may want to draw diagrams to show what's going on. (The picture at the beginning of this assignment shows what the situation in Question 1 might look like.)

1. There are 3 mystery bags on one side of the balance and 51 ounces of lead weights on the other side.

2. There are 1 mystery bag and 42 ounces of weights on one side, and 100 ounces of weights on the other side.

3. There are 8 mystery bags and 10 ounces of weights on one side, and 90 ounces of weights on the other side.

4. There are 3 mystery bags and 29 ounces of weights on one side, and 4 mystery bags on the other side.

5. There are 11 mystery bags and 65 ounces of weights on one side, and 4 mystery bags and 100 ounces of weights on the other side.

6. There are 6 mystery bags and 13 ounces of weights on one side, and 6 mystery bags and 14 ounces of weights on the other side. (The jester could get in a lot of trouble for this one!)

7. There are 15 mystery bags and 7 ounces of weights on both sides. (At first, the king thought this one was easy, but then he found it to be incredibly hard.)

8. The king wants to be able to win easily all of the time, without calling you in. Therefore, your final task in this assignment is to describe in words a procedure by which the king can find out how much is in a mystery bag in any situation.

Homework 7

You're the Jester

1. Here are some simple equations that might have come from mystery bags games. Solve each equation for M, which represents the weight of each mystery bag.

   a. $M + 16 = 43$

   b. $12M = 60$

   c. $27 + 9M = 90$

2. The equations in the next group are a bit more complicated. For each equation, do two things.

   • Describe how the jester must place the mystery bags and lead weights so that the equation will be a representation of the situation.

   • Find the weight of one mystery bag and explain how you got the answer.

   a. $5M + 24 = 51 + 2M$

   b. $43M + 37 = 56M + 24$

   c. $12M + 15 = 5M + 62$

3. Make up two equations of your own like those in Question 2. Describe the jester's setup for each of your equations, and find the weight of one mystery bag in each case.

Substitution and Evaluation

You often need to find out what the numerical value of a particular algebraic expression would be if you replaced the variable with a number. This happens a lot in the guess-and-check approach to solving equations.

It's useful to identify and name two separate parts of this process of getting numerical values from algebraic expressions.

- **Substitution** is the step of replacing the variable with a number.

- **Evaluation** is the step of getting a single number from the result of the substitution step.

For example, consider the expression $x^2 + 5x - 3$. Suppose you wanted to see what would happen if x were equal to 7.

Continued on next page

Substitution: In the substitution step, you simply replace each occurrence of the variable with the number 7, as shown here. Recall that 5(7) means 5 *times* 7.

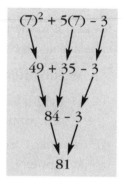

Notice that the number 7 has been placed within parentheses in each case for clarity. This isn't always necessary, but it helps prevent mistakes, such as getting 57 instead of $5 \cdot 7$.

Evaluation: The evaluation step turns the numerical expression $(7)^2 + 5(7) - 3$ into a single numerical value. As shown here, you might first replace $(7)^2$ with 49 and 5(7) with 35, then add $49 + 35$ to get 84, and finally subtract 3 from 84 to get the final result.

Here are some useful ways to express this overall process in words.

"The value of the expression $x^2 + 5x - 3$ for $x = 7$ is 81."

"Substituting 7 for x in the expression $x^2 + 5x - 3$ gives the value 81."

"Evaluating $x^2 + 5x - 3$ at $x = 7$ gives 81."

Keep in mind that in doing the evaluation step, you need to follow the rules for order of operations. By convention, we simplify expressions according to this sequence:

1. Parentheses
2. Exponents
3. Multiplication and division (equal priority) from left to right
4. Addition and subtraction (equal priority) from left to right

Warning: The Missing Multiplication Sign

According to the rules for order of operations, we apply an exponent before we multiply. For example, the numerical expression $3 \cdot 7^2$ means $3 \cdot 49$, and not 21^2.

This rule also governs algebraic expressions, but many errors in the substitution/evaluation process occur because we leave out multiplication signs in algebraic expressions. For example, in the expression $3x^2$, there is a "missing multiplication sign" between 3 and x^2. In other words, $3x^2$ is shorthand for $3 \cdot x^2$.

Therefore, $3x^2$ means $3 \cdot (x^2)$ and not $(3 \cdot x)^2$. You may find it helpful to insert parentheses or explicit multiplication signs into algebraic expressions in order to be clear about what they mean.

Homework 8

Letters, Numbers, and a Story

Part I: Substitution and Evaluation

Evaluate each of the eight expressions shown here according to these two steps.

- Replace the variable with the value shown, writing the resulting expression in complete detail.

- Compute the numerical value of the expression you get in the first step.

Be sure to insert parentheses or multiplication signs where needed.

Note: The instructions in Questions 1 through 8 illustrate some of the many ways by which the process of substitution is described. In each case, you should use both steps.

1. Evaluate $5 + 6q$ at $q = 9$.

2. Find the value of $3z + 20$ when $z = -8$.

3. Get the numerical value of $15 - 4x$ for $x = -1$.

4. Evaluate $3t^2 + 7$ if $t = -2$.

5. What is $-r^2$ when $r = 8$?

6. Find $-z^2$ with $z = -6$.

7. Substitute $k = 3$ into $3 \cdot 2^k + 5$.

8. Evaluate $3x^3 + (4x)^2$ using $x = 5$.

Part II: Make Up a Story

Create a situation and then write a question about your situation so that solving the equation $4(x + 3) = 40$ will answer your question. Be sure to identify what the variable x represents in your situation. Once you solve the equation, explain what the solution means in terms of your situation.

Catching Up

The Sawyer family is 120 miles behind the rest of the wagon train and needs to catch up. Both the wagon train and the Sawyers' wagon travel at about 3 miles per hour.

The Sawyer family realizes that in order to make up the difference, they will have to travel more hours each day. They know that the wagon train travels 8 hours each day. Therefore, the Sawyer family decides that they will travel 10 hours every day.

1. a. How far will the Sawyer family travel in 6 days?

   b. How far will the wagon train travel during those 6 days?

   c. Will the Sawyer family catch up in 6 days? Explain your answer.

2. a. How far will the Sawyer family travel in 15 days?

   b. How far will the wagon train travel during those 15 days?

   c. Will the Sawyer family catch up in 15 days?

3. Use *N* to represent a number of days.

   a. Write an expression for how far the Sawyer family will travel in *N* days.

   b. Write an expression for how far the wagon train will travel during those *N* days.

   c. Write an equation that states that the Sawyer family has caught up to the wagon train.

   d. Solve your equation from Question 3c and interpret the result.

Homework 9   More Letters, Numbers, and Mystery Bags

Part I: Substitution and Evaluation

1. As in *Homework 8: Letters, Numbers, and a Story,* evaluate each of these expressions showing these two steps.

   • Replace the variable by the value shown.

   • Compute the numerical value of the resulting expression.

   a. Find the value of $5a^2 + 3a + 4$ for $a = -2$.

   b. Evaluate $-r^3 + 2r^2 + 4r$ when $r = -3$.

   c. What is $(m^2 + 2)(m - 1) - (m - 1)(m^2 + 3)$ if $m = -7$?

   d. Substitute $c = -5$ into the expression $6(c + 4) - 3c(c - 1)$.

   e. Get the numerical value of $(v + 5)(v^2 - 4) - (v - 5)(v^2 + 4)$ at $v = 7$.

   f. Evaluate $y^3 + (2y)^2$ at $y = -5$.

   g. Find $2r^2 - 5r + 9$ with $r = -6$.

Continued on next page

2. Make up two substitution examples of your own using these steps.

- Decide what letter to use as the variable.

- Make up an expression using that variable.

- Pick a number to substitute as a value for the variable.

- Substitute the number for the variable and then evaluate the resulting expression.

In one of your examples, substitute a positive number. In the other example, substitute a negative number.

Part II: More Mystery Bags

3. Solve each of these equations and explain your work using the mystery-bags model.

a. $15M + 43 = 37M + 12$

b. $52x + 19 = 23 + 16x$

c. $5t + 12t + 13 = 8t + 19$

d. $9a + 6 + 3a + 7 = 10a + 21 + 6a$

e. $3r + 4 + 2r = 7 + r + 4r$

Back to the Lake

The following problem is from *Homework 4: Running on the Overland Trail.*

> Yolanda jogged 2 miles to a lake, jogged twice around the lake, and then jogged 2 more miles home. Altogether she traveled 10 miles. How far is it around the lake?

In that particular situation, the distance around the lake was 3 miles.

Well, Yolanda always does a 10-mile jog, and she likes to go 2 miles to the lake and 2 miles back, but she gets tired of always going around the lake twice. Fortunately, Yolanda lives in Minnesota, and several lakes of varying sizes are 2 miles from her home. She would like to be able to choose a lake of the right size depending on how many times she wants to go around.

1. Suppose Yolanda wants to jog 2 miles to a lake, go *four* times around it, jog 2 miles home, and have that be a total of 10 miles. How big a lake should she choose? That is, how far should it be around the lake?

Continued on next page

2. Now set up an In-Out table to describe situations like Yolanda's original jog and Question 1. In each case, Yolanda jogs 2 miles to a lake, goes some number of times around it, and jogs 2 miles home, for a total of 10 miles. The *In* for your table should be the number of times Yolanda goes around the lake, and the *Out* should be the distance around the lake.

a. Use Yolanda's original situation for one row of the table and Question 1 for another. (For instance, for the original situation, the *In* would be 2, because she went around twice, and the *Out* would be 3, because the distance around the lake was 3 miles.)

b. Create two more rows by choosing two other values for the *In*.

3. Now find a rule for your In-Out table from Question 2. Use *N* for the *In* and *d* for the *Out*, and write *d* as a function of *N*. In other words, write an equation in the form

$$d = \text{an expression involving } N$$

so that Yolanda could substitute any value she wanted for *N* and find the size of the lake she needs.

4. Make a graph based on the In-Out table from Question 2, using your equation from Question 3 to find more points for the graph.

Homework 10   What Will It Answer?

An important part of understanding what an equation or function means is knowing what types of questions it can be used to answer. For instance, the equation $A = s^2$ gives the area of a square (A) as a function of the length of its side (s).

The simplest use of this equation is to answer the question "What is the area of the square?" when you know the length of its side. For example, if you know that the length of a side is 5 inches, then you can substitute 5 for s to find that the area of the square is 5^2 (or 25) square inches.

The equation $A = s^2$ is even more powerful when you realize that it can also be used to answer a different type of question. That is, it can answer the question "What is the length of the side of the square?" if you know the square's area. For example, if you know that the area is 49 square inches, then the equation tells you that $49 = s^2$, which means that the side length must be 7 inches. (Why doesn't a solution of $s = -7$ make sense, even though it fits the equation $49 = s^2$?)

Continued on next page

1. The *perimeter* of a square is also a function of the length of a side.

   a. Choose variables and use them to write an equation describing this function. Be sure to state what your variables stand for.

   b. Give specific examples of two different types of questions that your equation can be used to answer. Also give the answers to your questions.

2. A movie theater charges $7 per ticket, and the theater's expenses are $500.

   a. Define appropriate variables and write an equation that gives the theater's profit as a function of the number of tickets sold. (Ignore such factors as the sale of refreshments.)

   b. Give specific examples of two different types of questions that your equation can be used to answer. Also give the answers to your questions.

Many principles in physics can be described in terms of functions. Questions 3 and 4 give two examples of this.

3. If an object is dropped and falls toward the ground, the distance it travels in t seconds is given approximately by the equation $d = 16t^2$, where d is the distance traveled, measured in feet. Come up with two different types of questions that this equation can be used to answer, and give the answers to your questions.

4. Newton's Second Law of Motion states that the force acting on an object (F) is equal to the object's mass (m) times the object's acceleration (a). In other words, the equation $F = ma$ gives the force as a function of mass and acceleration. What types of questions can this function be used to answer?

POW 2   *Tying the Knots*

Keekerik is an imaginary land where the people have an interesting three-stage ritual for couples who want to get married. Wandalina and Gerik are in that situation, so they go to the home of Queen Katalana to perform this ritual. Permission for them to marry as soon as they wish depends on the outcome of the ritual.

Stage 1: Loose Ends Top and Bottom

The queen greets them and reaches into a colorful box to pull out six identical strings for the ritual. The queen hands the strings to Wandalina, who holds them firmly in her fist. One end of each string is sticking out above Wandalina's fist, and the other end of each string is sticking out below her fist.

Stage 2: The Tops Are Tied

The queen steps to the side, and Gerik is called forward. He ties two of the ends together above Wandalina's fist. Then he ties two other ends above her fist together. Finally, he ties the last two ends above her fist together. The six ends below Wandalina's fist are still hanging untied.

Stage 3: The Bottoms Are Tied

Now Queen Katalana comes forward again. Although she was watching Gerik, she has no idea which string end below Wandalina's fist belongs to which end above. The queen does the final step. She randomly picks two of the ends below and ties them together, then two more, and finally the last two. So Wandalina now has six strings in her fist, with three knots above and three knots below.

Continued on next page

Will They Be Able to Marry?

Whether Wandalina and Gerik will be allowed to marry right away depends on what happens when Wandalina opens her fist. If the six strings form one large loop, then they will. Otherwise, they will be required to wait and repeat the ritual in six months.

With this in mind, think about these questions.

1. When Wandalina opens her fist and looks at the strings, what combinations of different size loops might there be?

2. What is the probability that the strings will form one big loop? In other words, what are the chances that Wandalina and Gerik will be able to marry right away?

3. What is the probability for each of the other possible combinations?

Although you may want to do some experiments to get some ideas about these questions, your answers for Questions 2 and 3 should involve discussion of the theoretical probability for each result, and not just experimental evidence.

Write-up

1. *Problem Statement*

2. *Process:* Explain how you worked on this problem, including what experiments you performed and how you kept track of your results.

3. *Solution:* Give the probability for each possible outcome and explain how you determined each probability.

4. *Evaluation*

5. *Self-assessment*

Homework 11

Line It Up

Probably the most important single type of function is the **linear function,** which can be defined as a function whose graph is a straight line.

1. Consider the function *f* defined by the equation

$$f(x) = 3x + 2$$

   a. Find each of the values $f(1), f(2),$ and $f(3)$.

   b. Use the results of Question 1a to complete this partial In-Out table for the function *f*.

x	f(x)
1	?
2	?
3	?

   c. Graph the points from your In-Out table.

   d. Do you think the graph of *f* is a straight line? In other words, is *f* a linear function? Explain your answer.

2. a. Plot the two points $(2, 3)$ and $(4, 7)$.

   b. Draw a straight line through your two points and find a third point on that line.

   c. Make an In-Out table like the one shown here, using your point from Question 2b as the third row.

In	Out
2	3
4	7
?	?

   d. Find a rule for your table in Question 2c.

3. What kind of algebraic expression do you think can be used as the rule for a linear function? (You might either give some examples or try to provide a general description.)

The Graph Solves the Problem

In Question 2 of *Homework 10: What Will It Answer?* you probably came up with an equation like $p = 7t - 500$ to describe the theater's profit (p) in terms of the number of tickets they sold (t).

In Question 3 of that assignment, you were given the equation $d = 16t^2$ to describe d, the distance an object has fallen (in feet), in terms of t, the time elapsed (in seconds).

Use these two equations and the graphing feature of your graphing calculator to answer these questions.

1. a. The theater made a profit of $277 on yesterday's show. How many tickets were sold?

    b. Three hundred people bought tickets for today's show. How much profit did the theater make?

2. a. An object is dropped off the roof of a very tall building. How long will it take for the object to fall 200 feet?

    b. How far will the object have gone if it falls for 6 seconds?

Note: You may find that you want to use a method other than graphing to answer these questions. If so, use that method to *check* your answer *after* you have used the graph.

Homework 12

Who's Right?

1. Andrew and Gladys were working on rules for In-Out tables. When they got to the table shown here, Andrew said that the *Out* at the bottom should be 2(X + 1). Gladys said it should be 2X + 2. You need to decide who is right. Study the table and think about other In-Out pairs of numbers that you think would fit the pattern.

In	Out
3	8
5	12
9	20
15	32
X	?

   If you think that either Andrew or Gladys is wrong, or that both are wrong, explain why you think so. If you think that they are both right, explain how there could be two different answers.

2. Find the area of each of the shapes shown here. That is, find out how many 1-foot–by–1-foot squares will fit in each without overlapping. Assume that all angles are right angles. *Do not assume* that these drawings are to scale.

   a.
   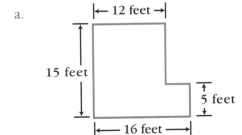

   b.
   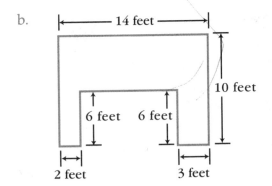

What's the Same?

In everyday language, we can usually say the same thing in many different ways. This is also true about the language of algebra. Algebraic expressions that say the same thing are called "equivalent."

In mathematical work, you often need to be able to switch smoothly from one algebraic expression to an equivalent one. In the next section of this unit, you'll be looking at ways to do this and at how to use equivalent expressions to solve equations. You may be surprised to see that you can often use geometry to find equivalent algebraic expressions.

Sofia Anis and Molly Berglund take delight in challenging the class to solve some of the equations they have scrambled.

A Lot of Changing Sides

A housing developer submitted plans to the city planner for some houses she wanted to build. The lots in the plan were all squares of the same size. But the city planner thought that this plan was boring and insisted that the developer introduce some variety. After some discussion, the planner and the developer decided that the lots should include other types of rectangles. So the developer proceeded to change the lengths of some of the sides of the lots.

For each of the changes that were made to the square lots, complete these tasks.

- Make and label a sketch of the lot, using the variable X to represent the length of a side of the original square.

- Write an expression for the area of the new lot as a product of its length and width.

- Write an expression *without parentheses* for the area of the new lot as a sum of smaller areas. Use your sketch to explain this expression.

1. The original square lot was extended 4 meters in one direction and 3 meters in the other.

2. The original square lot was extended 5 meters in one direction only.

3. The original square lot was extended 10 meters in one direction and 9 meters in the other.

4. The original square lot was extended 1 meter in one direction and 25 meters in the other.

5. The original square lot was extended 2 meters in one direction and decreased 2 meters in the other.

Homework 13   Why Are They Equivalent?

You saw in *Homework 12: Who's Right?* that the two expressions $2(X + 1)$ and $2X + 2$ seem to give the same result no matter what number is substituted for X. In other words, the expressions appear to be equivalent. But it would be nice to be certain of this and to understand *why* the expressions are equivalent.

Randy, Sandy, and Dandy were having just that discussion. Read each of their explanations, and then do these four things.

1. Decide whether any, all, or just some of them are correct, and explain your decision.

2. State which explanation is the easiest for you to understand, and why.

3. State which explanation is most convincing to you, and why.

4. Adapt the explanation you understand best to explain in your own words why the expressions $3(X + 4)$ and $3X + 12$ are equivalent.

Randy's Explanation

"We all know that $2A$ is twice A, which is $A + A$. Think of $2(X + 1)$ as being twice $X + 1$. In other words, it is equal to $(X + 1) + (X + 1)$. And $(X + 1) + (X + 1)$ is equal to $2X + 2$."

Continued on next page

Sandy's Explanation

"It works with numbers! Check it out! If X is 5, then $2(X + 1)$ is $2(5 + 1)$, which is the same as $2 \cdot 6$, which is 12. And, well, $2X + 2$ is $2 \cdot 5 + 2$, which is the same as $10 + 2$, which is also 12! Wow!"

Dandy's Explanation

"Multiplication is how you find the area of a rectangle, you know, length times width. Basically, a product ab can be thought of as the area of a rectangle with dimensions a and b, like this:

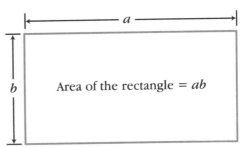

"The product $2(X + 1)$ can represent the area of a rectangle that is 2 units in one dimension and $X + 1$ units in the other. The length of $X + 1$ is like a segment of length X next to a segment of length 1. The picture is something like this:

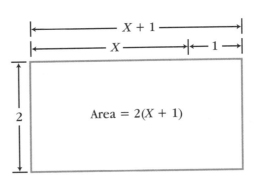

"A simple dividing line shows that this figure can be thought of as two rectangles, with areas $2X$ and 2, put together. Because we are talking about the same area, $2(X + 1)$ must equal $2X + 2$."

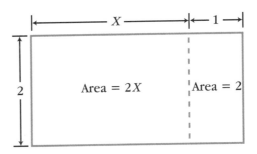

Homework 14

One Each Way

1. Find an equivalent expression without parentheses for each of these expressions.

   a. $5(A + 7)$

   b. $8(y - 4)$

   c. $2(W + 6)$

2. In *Homework 13: Why Are They Equivalent?* you saw three ways of thinking about why $2(X + 1)$ is equivalent to $2X + 2$. Now use those ideas to explain your work in Question 1.

   a. Use Randy's *repeated addition* method to explain why your answer to Question 1a is equivalent to $5(A + 7)$.

   b. Use Sandy's *numerical example* method to explain why your answer to Question 1b is equivalent to $8(y - 4)$.

   c. Use Dandy's *area model* method to explain why your answer to Question 1c is equivalent to $2(W + 6)$.

3. Find an equivalent expression without parentheses for each of these expressions. Use any method you like, but explain your work.

   a. $(r + 4)(r + 3)$

   b. $(3t + 1)(t + 5)$

Distributing the Area

The figure on the right is a large rectangle made up of some smaller rectangles. The measurements of the smaller rectangles are shown using the variables *a*, *b*, *c*, and *d*.

Remember that you can compute the area of a rectangle by multiplying its length by its width.

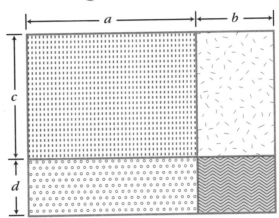

1. Use the "length times width" area formula and the variables *a*, *b*, *c*, and *d* to write an expression for the area of each of the smaller rectangles from the diagram.

a. Area of the rectangle shaded like [figure] = –?–

b. Area of the rectangle shaded like [figure] = –?–

c. Area of the rectangle shaded like [figure] = –?–

d. Area of the rectangle shaded like [figure] = –?–

Continued on next page

2. Next, look at certain combinations of rectangles and write each area in two ways.

   • As the product of its length and width

   • As the sum of two smaller areas

   a. Area of the figure shaded like  = –?–

   b. Area of the figure shaded like  = –?–

3. Write the area of the entire rectangle in *at least* two ways.

4. a. Draw and label a rectangle whose area can be written as the product $(p + q + r)(x + y + z)$.

   b. Show how to use your diagram to write the product $(p + q + r)(x + y + z)$ as an expression without parentheses.

5. *Challenge:* Draw a diagram that could be used as a model for finding an expression without parentheses that is equivalent to $(a + b)^3$. (*Hint:* We can't call it an *area* model.)

Homework 15   The Distributive Property and Mystery Lots

Part I: The Distributive Property

In its simplest form, the distributive property says that the expressions $a(x + y)$ and $ax + ay$ are equivalent. In other words, according to the distributive property, the equation

$$a(x + y) = ax + ay$$

is true no matter what numbers are substituted for a, x, and y.

Sometimes this property is used to replace an expression with parentheses by an equivalent expression without parentheses. For example, you can write $5(2x + 3)$ as $10x + 15$. This use of the distributive property is often called **multiplying through.** We also sometimes say that the factor 5 has been "distributed" across the sum $2x + 3$.

Continued on next page

1. Distribute the factor across each sum.

 a. $4(a + 9)$

 b. $3(5w + 2r)$

 c. $6t(2 + 3s)$

 d. $10c(u + v + w)$

The distributive property is also used in the reverse direction from the examples of Question 1. For instance, you can write $8x + 12y$ as $4(2x + 3y)$. This use of the distributive property is often called **taking out a common factor** (or just *factoring*). You might want to think of this as "undistributing."

2. Take out a common factor in each of these sums.

 a. $14d + 21e$

 b. $rg + rh$

 c. $2pq + 4pr$

 d. $6ab + 10ac$

Part II: Mystery Lots

The developer from *A Lot of Changing Sides* has taken to writing plans for lot sizes in algebraic code. Unfortunately, the codes are giving the city planner a hard time.

3. Here is what the city planner found written in the developer's notes one day:

 "Build a lot whose area is $X^2 + 3X + 5X + 15$."

 Help the city planner by finding out what the developer planned to do with the original square lot. (Remember that the original lot had sides of length X.)

4. What do you suppose each of these two entries means?

 a. "Build a lot whose area is $X^2 + 4X + 6X + 24$."

 b. "Build a lot whose area is $X^2 + 6X + 2X + 12$."

5. Then the developer's entries got even more cryptic. Figure out for the city planner what each of these entries means.

 a. "Build a lot whose area is $X^2 + 9X + 18$."

 b. "Build a lot whose area is $X^2 + 7X + 10$."

 c. "Build a lot whose area is $X^2 + 6X + 8$."

 d. "Build a lot whose area is $X^2 + 5X + 4$."

Homework 16   Views of the Distributive Property

The **distributive property** is an important general principle that can be used in many situations to write a mathematical expression in another form. Recall that in its simplest algebraic form, the distributive property can be expressed by an equation like this one.

$$a(x + y) = ax + ay$$

In words, you might state the distributive property this way.

> Multiplying a sum by something is the same as multiplying each term by that "something" and then adding the products.

In this assignment, you'll be looking at various ways to think about and use the distributive property.

Multidigit Multiplication

You may not have realized that you've been using the distributive property every time you do multiplication that involves more than one-digit numbers. For example, the product $73 \cdot 56$ can be thought of as $(70 + 3) \cdot 56$. Applying the distributive property, you would get $70 \cdot 56 + 3 \cdot 56$.

You might write this problem in vertical form.

$$
\begin{array}{r}
56 \\
\times 73 \\
\hline
168 \\
3920 \\
\hline
\end{array}
$$
   (this is $3 \cdot 56$)
   (this is $70 \cdot 56$)

Comment: People often omit the zero in 3920, simply multiplying $7 \cdot 56$ to get 392 and then writing 392 with the 2 lined up in the tens column.

Continued on next page

Each of the products 3 · 56 and 70 · 56 can also be found using the distributive property. To show all the details in the written multiplication, you might write it like this.

$$
\begin{array}{r}
56 \\
\times\, 73 \\
\hline
18 \\
150 \\
420 \\
3500 \\
\hline
\end{array}
$$

    18   (this is 3 · 6)

  150   (this is 3 · 50)

  420   (this is 70 · 6)

3500   (this is 70 · 50)

Each of the numbers 18, 150, 420, and 3500 is called a **partial product.** Writing a multidigit multiplication showing all the partial products is sometimes called the **long form.**

In the usual written form of this problem, the partial products 18 and 150 are not shown individually. Instead, their sum, 168, is written. Similarly, we omit the partial products 420 and 3500 and simply write their sum, 3920. The numbers 168 and 3920, which are each the sum of two partial products, are sometimes referred to as **partial sums.**

1. Show how to find the product 32 · 94 using the long form, showing all the partial products.

Multiplication with a Diagram

You can illustrate the product 73 · 56 with an area diagram like this one, in which each smaller rectangle represents one of the partial products. Notice that the areas of the two smaller rectangles on the right add up to the partial sum 168 while the areas of the two larger rectangles on the left add up to the partial sum 3920.

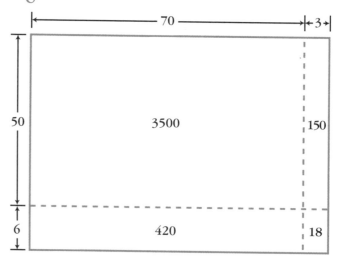

Continued on next page

2. Draw an area diagram like the one shown on the previous page to illustrate the product 32 · 94.

3. Show how to find the product 47 · 619 in two ways.

    a. Using the long form

    b. Using an area diagram

Multiplying in Algebra Is Like Multiplying in Arithmetic

Multiplication of algebraic expressions can be done in a way that is similar to multidigit multiplication. For example, you can set up the problem $(x + 3)(2x + 5)$ in vertical form.

$$2x + 5$$
$$\underline{\times \ \ x + 3}$$

As with 73 · 56, this problem involves four separate products.

4. a. Find this product using a vertical multiplication form. You can use either the long form or a shorter form.

    b. Show how to do this problem using an area diagram.

Prime Time

A **prime number** (also called simply a *prime*) is a whole number that has exactly two whole-number divisors: 1 and itself. For example, 7 is a prime number, because it has exactly two whole-number divisors: 1 and 7. On the other hand, 10 is not a prime, because it has four whole-number divisors: 1, 2, 5, and 10. A nonzero whole number with more than two whole-number divisors is called a **composite number.**

The number 1 is *not* considered a prime, because it has only one whole-number divisor, nor is it a composite number. Rather, it is considered a special case.

1. Examine each of the numbers from 2 through 30.

   a. Make a list of the numbers in this group that are primes.

   b. For each composite number from 2 through 30, write that number as a product of prime numbers. This is called the **prime factorization.** *Note:* You may need to use more than two factors, and you can use the same factor more than once. For example, the prime factorization of 12 is the product 2 · 2 · 3.

2. If an expression from Question 1b used a factor more than once, rewrite the expression using an exponent instead of repeating the factor. For example, write 12 as $2^2 \cdot 3$ instead of 2 · 2 · 3.

POW 3   *Divisor Counting*

As you saw in *Prime Time,* a prime number is a whole number that has exactly two whole-number divisors. This POW is about counting the divisors for any whole number—not only primes. Throughout this problem, the word *divisor* will mean *whole-number* divisor.

The number 1 is a divisor of every whole number and every whole number is a divisor of itself. Therefore, every whole number greater than 1 has at least two distinct divisors and so must either be a prime or have more than two divisors. Your task in this POW is to figure out as much as you can about *how many* divisors a number has. You will probably find the concept of prime numbers useful both in conducting your investigation and in stating your conclusions.

Continued on next page

Here are some examples of questions to look at.

- What kinds of numbers have *exactly* three divisors? *exactly* four? and so on.

- Do bigger numbers necessarily have more divisors?

- Is there a way to figure out how many divisors 1,000,000 (one million) has without actually listing and counting them? How about 1,000,000,000 (one billion)?

- What's the smallest number that has 20 divisors?

But you should not answer only these questions. You should also come up with your own questions and look for generalizations.

Write-up

1. *Subject of Exploration:* What were you exploring? What were your goals?

2. *Questions:* What questions did you ask yourself? Why did you ask them? Which ones did you decide to explore?

3. *Information Gathering:* Based on your notes, describe what you did to get data for your exploration.

   a. How did you get started?

   b. What approaches did you try?

   c. What information did you gather?

   d. When did you decide to stop, and why?

4. *Results and Conjectures:* What conjectures did you find as possible answers to your questions? What rules or patterns did you find in exploring your questions? If you can prove that your conjectures are right, do so. If you can explain why a particular rule or pattern works, do that as well. If possible, generalize your results.

5. *Evaluation*

6. *Self-assessment*

Homework 17

Exactly Three or Four

1. By definition, a number with exactly two whole-number divisors is a prime number. But what about numbers with exactly three whole-number divisors? Or exactly four?

   To get you started on *POW 3: Divisor Counting,* your first task in this assignment is to consider these two special cases.

   a. Find several numbers that each have exactly three divisors and several others that each have exactly four divisors.

   b. Examine your two lists and look for some explanations or patterns.

2. Decide on at least one specific question about divisors that you want to try to answer as part of your POW, and state that question as clearly as you can.

Taking Some Out, Part I

Do you remember the chefs from *Patterns* in Year 1? You used their situation to help with the arithmetic of positive and negative numbers. Well, thinking about temperatures can also be of help when finding equivalent expressions.

In each of the problems here, you should assume that when the action begins, the temperature of the cauldron is 0 degrees. As usual, every hot cube added to the cauldron increases the temperature by one degree and every hot cube removed from the cauldron lowers the temperature by one degree.

1. The chefs decided to put 50 hot cubes into the cauldron, but once they did so, they found that the cauldron was too hot. So two of the chefs reached in and removed some hot cubes. One chef removed a batch of 5 hot cubes and the other chef removed a batch of 10 hot cubes.

    a. What was the temperature when this was all done?

Continued on next page

b. Write the entire process as a chef instruction in two ways:

- With parentheses, showing the two batches of cubes being removed together

- Without parentheses, showing the two batches of cubes being removed one batch at a time

2. Another time the chefs put 45 hot cubes into the cauldron and again found that the cauldron was too hot. Two chefs removed some hot cubes. One chef took out a batch of 8 hot cubes and the other took out a batch of 11 hot cubes.

a. What was the temperature at the end of this process?

b. As in Question 1b, write the entire process as a chef instruction in two ways.

3. The next time this happened, the chefs put in 60 hot cubes to begin with, and again two chefs took some out. The first chef removed a batch of 9 hot cubes, but the second chef forgot to count the number of cubes he removed.

a. Create several rows for an In-Out table in which the *In* is the number of hot cubes the second chef removed and the *Out* is the final temperature.

b. Find two rules for the table—one with parentheses and one without parentheses. Use *X* to represent the *In*.

c. Graph your two rules on the graphing calculator and see if they give you the same graph.

Homework 18   Subtracting Some Sums

1. Write each of these expressions as an equivalent expression without parentheses. Simplify your results where you can by combining like terms.

   a. $35 - (3a + 14)$

   b. $50 - (c + 17 + 2d)$

   c. $16 + 9s - (3s + 11)$

   d. $23 + 5w - 2(w + 7)$

2. The equations in the next series involve subtracting a sum that is in parentheses. Use whatever techniques make sense to you to solve these equations, but write an explanation of what you do.

   a. $54 - (t + 5) = 32$

   b. $29 - 2(x + 4) = 5$

   c. $6z + 17 - (2z + 5) = 56$

Continued on next page

Solve It!

3. Because the distributive property is so important in working with algebraic expressions, it's helpful to be able to apply it smoothly and with confidence. Find each of the products below, writing the results without parentheses and combining like terms when possible.

   a. $(x + 4)(x + 7)$

   b. $(2t + 3)(3t - 5)$

   c. $(4r - 3)(3r - 2)$

   d. $(x^2 + 3x + 2)(x + 6)$

4. Soon you'll be combining ideas about equivalent expressions with your insights learned from work with the mystery bags in order to solve more complex equations. In preparation for that, here are some mystery bag problems for you. Solve these equations to find out how much gold is in each mystery bag.

   a. $26M + 37 = 19M + 58$

   b. $46a + 95 = 83a + 29$

   c. $153x + 149 = 327x + 73$

Taking Some Out, Part II

The chefs are continuing to play around with their cauldron. Use each of these problems to investigate ways to write different expressions for the same situation. As in *Taking Some Out, Part I,* each situation begins with a temperature of 0 degrees.

1. The chefs tossed 75 hot cubes into the cauldron. A few minutes later, one of the chefs reached in to remove some of them. She already had 12 hot cubes in her hands when she stumbled and 4 of those hot cubes fell back in.

   a. What was the temperature at the end of this process?

   b. Using the numbers in the problem, write the entire process in two ways.

   • Show the initial amount put in and subtract an expression in parentheses to show what was removed altogether.

   • Show the initial amount put in, use subtraction to show the whole batch of cubes being removed, and use addition to show some of that batch going back in. Your expression should not have parentheses.

Continued on next page

2. The next time, 62 hot cubes were put in originally. A chef then removed 14 of them, but 9 of the 14 fell back into the cauldron.

   a. What was the temperature at the end of this process?

   b. As in Question 1b, write the entire process in two ways.

3. The third time, 54 hot cubes initially were tossed in. A chef reached in and grabbed 25 of them, but first 6 of the 25 and then 4 more fell back in.

   a. What was the temperature at the end of this process?

   b. Write this entire process in *at least three* different ways.

4. Once again, the chefs tossed a big batch of hot cubes into the cauldron. Someone reached into the cauldron and pulled a handful of them out, but part of that handful fell back in. Write two different general expressions, one with parentheses and one without, describing what happened. Use different variables to represent the initial amount put in, the amount initially removed, and the amount that fell back in.

Homework 19

Randy, Sandy, and Dandy Return

Part I: Generalizing the Distributive Property

Randy, Sandy, and Dandy are having another of their heated arguments. This time they aren't discussing why the distributive property is true, but are trying to find other principles that might be based on similar reasoning.

1. Randy says, "I use the distributive property all the time, even when it just involves multiplication." In other words, Randy thinks that $a(bc) = (ab) \cdot (ac)$.

   Is she correct? Try substituting some numbers to find out. If she's right, explain why. If she's wrong, rewrite the right side of the equation to make her statement correct.

2. Sandy then says, "I use the distributive property all the time, too." (This makes Randy worry a little about what she thinks.) "And I use it with additions all over the place." What Sandy thinks is that $a + (b + c) = (a + b) + (a + c)$.

   Is she correct? Try substituting some numbers to find out. If she's right, explain why. If she's wrong, rewrite the right side of the equation to make her statement correct.

3. Dandy thinks they are both confused and says, "I don't know what you two are thinking of, but I know that $a - (b - c) = a - b + c$."

   Is he correct? Try substituting some numbers to find out. If he's right, explain why. If he's wrong, rewrite the right side of the equation to make his statement correct.

Part II: Distributing Mystery Bags

4. For each of the equations shown here, first use the distributive property (correctly!) to remove the parentheses on each side of the equation, and then combine terms on each side and solve the resulting equation.

   a. $4(M + 2) + 7 = 6(M + 1) + 2$

   b. $3(x + 9) + 2(3x + 4) = 7(x + 11)$

   c. $5(2x - 3) + 3(x + 8) = 4(x + 6) + 3(x - 4)$

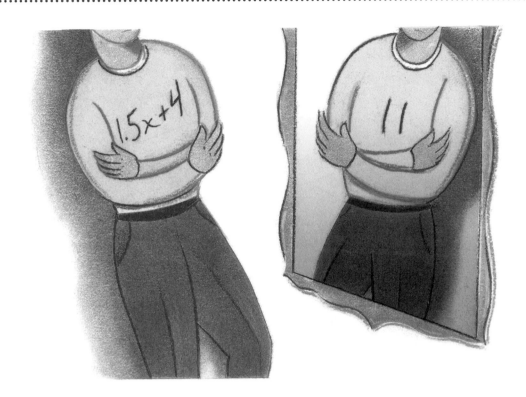

Homework 20   Equation Time

Equations play an important role in mathematics, and the concept of equivalent equations is a valuable tool in solving equations. These problems give you a chance to apply some of what you know about equivalent equations.

1. A student trying to solve the equation $1.5x + 4 = 11$ wrote what is shown below. Is this correct? If not, why not?

$$1.5x + 4 = 11$$

$$3x + 4 = 22 \quad \text{(multiplying both sides by 2)}$$

$$3x = 18 \quad \text{(subtracting 4 from both sides)}$$

$$x = 6 \quad \text{(dividing both sides by 3)}$$

2. In your work with similar triangles, you have used a particular type of equation called a *proportion,* which is a statement that two ratios are equal.

Continued on next page

For example, if you know that the two quadrilaterals shown here are similar, you might come up with the proportion

$$\frac{x}{5} = \frac{x + 2}{8}$$

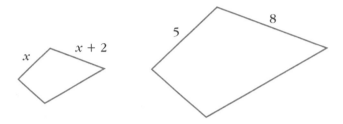

One of the principles for getting equivalent equations is that you can multiply both sides of the equation by the same thing.

a. Apply this principle to the equation $\frac{x}{5} = \frac{x+2}{8}$, first multiplying both sides by 5 and then multiplying both sides of the result by 8 (or simply multiply both sides by 40).

b. Simplify and solve the equation you got in Question 2a and check your solution in the original equation.

3. Solve each of these equations, explaining each step clearly.

a. $41 + 7d - 5(d + 7) = 8d + 1$

b. $8w - 3(2w - 9) = 7(w + 2)$

Scrambling Equations

Usually, the concept of equivalent equations is used to make things simpler. But in this activity, you're going to make things more complicated. For example, look at the sequence of equations shown below.

$$x = 1$$

$$6x = 6$$

$$6x - 3 = 3$$

$$\frac{6x - 3}{2} = 1.5$$

All of these equations are equivalent, because they all have the same solution. You should be able to see what was done to each equation to get the one below it.

In this activity, you will begin by writing down a *very simple* equation (like $x = 1$). Then you'll write down an equivalent equation that's more complicated, and then something equivalent to that, and so on.

Continued on next page

This activity has some very precise rules. You will be changing your equation exactly three times. At each stage, you can do any one of these four things.

- You can add the same integer to both sides of the equation.

- You can subtract the same integer from both sides of the equation.

- You can multiply both sides of the equation by the same nonzero integer.

- You can divide both sides of the equation by the same nonzero integer.

Remember that you are to do *exactly three* of these steps (in any order). For instance, the example shown above uses multiplication, then subtraction, and then division. At any time in the process, you're also allowed to do arithmetic steps to simplify the right side of the equation.

When you are done with this process, copy your final, complicated equation onto one side of a sheet of paper and put your original equation on the reverse side. This sheet will be exchanged with another group, and you will have the opportunity to "uncomplicate" someone else's scrambled equation.

Homework 21   More Scrambled Equations and Mystery Bags

Part I: More Scrambled Equations

This assignment involves the same steps for getting equivalent equations that were described in *Scrambling Equations*.

1. The equations here show one sequence of three steps to "scramble" the equation $x = 3$.

$$x = 3$$

$$x - 5 = 2$$

$$10(x - 5) = -20$$

$$\frac{10(x - 5)}{4} = -5$$

   a. Describe what was done at each step.

   b. Check that $x = 3$ is a solution to the final equation in the sequence, and show your work.

Continued on next page

For Questions 2 through 4, do two things

- "Uncomplicate" each equation until you get back to a simple equation of the form "x = some number."

- Take the value of x you get from the simple equation and substitute it back into the original equation in order to check that it makes the "complicated" equation true.

2. $3x - 5 = -2$

3. $\dfrac{x - 6}{4} + 1 = 7$

4. $4\left(\dfrac{x}{3} + 6\right) - 8 = 20$

Part II: More Mystery Bags

Earlier in this unit, you used the idea of a pan balance to solve mystery-bag problems.

The equations here might come from such problems. Solve them using the concept of equivalent equations, but also think about how each step you do is related to the pan-balance model.

5. $11t + 13 = 7t + 41$

6. $12 + 7w = 4w + 21$

7. $8(x + 3) + 19 = 15 + 2(x + 35)$

Days 22–26

The Linear World

A straight line is one of the simplest types of graphs. In *Homework 11: Line It Up,* you saw that certain algebraic expressions lead to graphs that are straight lines.

Linear equations and linear functions are important in many applications of mathematics, and you already know a great deal about them. In an activity called *Get It Straight,* you'll work with your classmates to learn even more.

Terria Galvez and Mekea Harvey continue their work on linear functions and straight-line graphs.

Old Friends and New Friends

Part I: Old Friends

Over the course of this unit, you have set up equations for a variety of problems. The examples here give brief reminders of some of those problems. With each problem is an equation that might have been used to help solve the problem.

Your task in this assignment is to solve these equations. Although you could probably solve them by trial and error or by graphing, you are to solve them here using equivalent equations. Show the steps you use to get from the equations to the solutions, and check your answers by substituting them back into the original equations. *Note:* Because these problems are stated here without details, you do not need to explain how each equation fits its problem.

1. Problem: Find the payoff that would give Al a total gain of 25 points (Question 3 from *Memories of Yesteryear*).

    Equation: $25x - 75 \cdot 2 = 25$

Continued on next page

2. Problem: Find the distance around the lake (Question 2 from *Homework 4: Running on the Overland Trail*).

   Equation: $2d + 4 = 10$

3. Problem: Find the number of days the Sawyers would need to catch up (Question 3 from *Catching Up*).

   Equation: $30N = 24N + 120$

4. Problem: Find the length of Nelson's shadow (Question 2 from *Lamppost Shadows*).

   Equation: $\dfrac{S}{S + 20} = \dfrac{6}{25}$

   (*Note:* This isn't exactly in the form of a linear equation, but it is essentially equivalent to a linear equation. You might look at Question 2 of *Homework 20: Equation Time* for ideas.)

Part II: New Friends

These equations don't come from specific problems, but that doesn't affect the algebra. Solve each of them using equivalent equations, and show the steps you use.

5. $4(t + 5) + 3 = 7t + 19$

6. $6W - (2W + 1) = 3(W - 10)$

Homework 22

New Friends Visit Your Home

Part I: Solve It!

As you've seen, linear equations come up in many situations. Sometimes the equations are simple, and sometimes they are complicated. Use the method of equivalent equations to solve each example here, and check your solutions by substituting into the original equations.

1. $7t - 5 = 10t + 8 - 4t$
2. $6(x - 2) = 4(x + 3) - 32$
3. $8r + 1 = 12r + 27$
4. $5(w + 4) - 3(w + 2) = 3(w + 3) - (w - 5)$
5. $6g - (3g + 8) = 16$
6. $7 - 4d = 3d - 9d + 25$
7. $6 + 4(y + 2) = 10 - 4y$

Part II: Write It!

Make up a situation for which the equation $5 + x = 21 - x$ might be appropriate. Identify what the variable represents in the situation you create.

Homework 23   From One Variable to Two

You've seen that a linear equation in one variable such as $3x + 4 = 2(x - 1)$ has a unique solution. The equation $x + 2y = 5 + 3x + y$ is also a linear equation, but it includes two variables and has more than one solution. This assignment looks at what it means to "solve" an equation like this.

1. Begin with the simpler two-variable equation, $y = 2x + 3$.

   a. Find at least three number pairs that fit this equation.

   b. Plot the number pairs you found in part a.

2. Now use the equation $x + 2y = 5 + 3x + y$.

   a. Find at least three number pairs that fit this equation. *Hint:* Pick a number for one of the variables and then find a value for the other variable that fits the equation.

   b. Plot the number pairs you found in part a.

3. Write an equation that is equivalent to $x + 2y = 5 + 3x + y$ but that expresses y in terms of x. In other words, your equation should have y by itself on the left and an expression involving x on the right. This is called **solving for y in terms of x.** *Suggestion:* Think of the equation as a mystery-bag problem in which x and y represent the weights for two different-size mystery bags.

Get It Straight

You know that any equation involving x and y can be used to create a graph. The graph is defined as the set of all those points whose coordinates fit the equation.

Some equations have graphs that are straight lines. These are called **linear equations.** When a linear equation expresses y in terms of x, it can be referred to as a **linear function.** All linear functions can be simplified so that they fit the form $y = ax + b$, where a and b represent two numbers.

The number a is referred to as the **coefficient of x** and the number b is called the **constant term.** Keep in mind that these numbers can be positive, negative, or zero, and they can also be identical.

In this activity, you will investigate linear functions and straight-line graphs.

Here are some questions to explore.

- How do you change the equation in order to change the "slant" of its graph?

- How do you change the equation in order to shift the whole graph up or down?

Continued on next page

Interactive Mathematics Program

- When do two linear functions give parallel lines (lines that never meet)? Why?

- What linear functions give horizontal lines? Why?

- When do two linear functions give lines that are mirror images of each other with the *y*-axis as the mirror? Why?

- When do two linear functions give perpendicular lines (lines that form a right angle)? Why?

Do not feel limited by these questions—let your imagination soar! Keep track of any other interesting questions you think of, even if you can't answer them.

Write-up

You should do a written report of what you learn, using these categories.

1. *Questions:* What questions did you ask yourself? Why did you ask them? Which ones did you decide to explore?

2. *Results and Conjectures:* What conjectures did you find as possible answers to your questions? What rules or patterns did you find in exploring your questions? If you can prove that your conjectures are right, do so. If you can explain why some rule or pattern works, do that as well. If possible, generalize your results.

Homework 24   A Distributive Summary

The distributive property played an important role in this unit. This assignment on that important idea will be part of your unit portfolio.

Write as complete an explanation of the distributive property as you can. You should touch on at least these issues.

• What it says

• Why it's true

• Examples of situations in which you would use it

Homework 25   All by Itself

You've seen that a linear equation in two variables can be transformed into a linear function by writing one of the variables in terms of the other variable. This assignment continues that theme.

1. In the activity *Fair Share on Chores* (from the Year 1 unit *The Overland Trail*), three boys and two girls were responsible for watching the animals for a total of ten hours, with the boys and the girls each having a shift of a certain length. (*Remember:* Families considered this fair in light of other chores the boys and girls had to do.)

   If B represents the length of each boy's shift and G represents the length of each girl's shift, then the fact that the total time is ten hours can be represented by the equation

   $$3B + 2G = 10$$

Continued on next page

Solve this equation for B in terms of G. In other words, find an equivalent equation of the form

$$B = \text{an expression involving } G$$

Hint: One approach is to imagine that you knew the length of each girl's shift (the value of G) and to think about how you would figure out the length of each boy's shift (the value of B).

2. In Question 1, you worked with a linear equation that came from the context of a real-life situation. In these examples, all you have are the equations. In each case, solve the equation for the specified variable.

   a. Solve this equation for v in terms of w.

   $$2v + 7 = w - 3$$

   b. Solve this equation for s in terms of r.

   $$4r + 5s + 2 = 8r - s + 7$$

   c. Solve this equation for y in terms of x.

   $$5y - 2x + 1 = 3(y + x) - (x - 5)$$

   d. Solve the equation from Question 2b for r in terms of s.

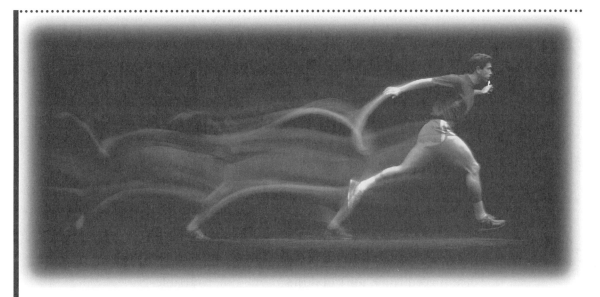

Homework 26   More Variable Solutions

In *Homework 25: All by Itself,* you looked at some linear equations and found equivalent equations expressing one variable in terms of another. In this assignment, only Question 1 involves a linear equation.

1. Solve this linear equation for z in terms of x.

$$3(x - z) - 2(5 - x) = 4z + 2 - 6(x + z)$$

On the remaining examples, you may find it useful to imagine that certain variables represent numbers or actually to replace them with numbers. Then think about how you would solve the given equation for the remaining variable. This approach is used in Question 2.

2. The kinetic energy of a moving object is given by the formula

$$W = \frac{1}{2} mv^2$$

where W represents the kinetic energy, m represents the mass of the object, and v is the object's velocity.

  a. Suppose $W = 30$ and $v = 3$. What is the numerical value of m? (Don't worry about the units involved for energy, mass, or velocity.)

  b. Use your work from Question 2a to solve the equation for m in terms of W and v.

Continued on next page

3. Solve the equation from Question 2 for v in terms of W and m.

4. Coulomb's law states that the force of attraction or repulsion between two electrical charges is proportional to the product of their charges and inversely proportional to the square of the distance between them. In symbols, Coulomb's law can be expressed by the equation

$$F = \frac{kq_1q_2}{r^2}$$

where F is the force, q_1 and q_2 are the charges, and r is the distance between them. The letter k represents a number called a **constant of proportionality.**

a. Solve this equation for q_1 in terms of the other variables.

b. Solve this equation for r in terms of the other variables.

Note: The small numbers 1 and 2 in the notation q_1 and q_2 are called **subscripts.** Subscripts are often used when several variables represent similar things in a problem situation. In this case, there are two particles with electric charges, and the sizes of the charges are each represented using a single variable consisting of the letter q and a subscript number.

Days 27–31

Beyond Linearity

So now you can solve any linear equation! But what about equations that aren't linear? Are there any systematic ways to solve them?

In the final segment of this unit, you'll see how useful graphs and graphing calculators can be in solving more complicated equations.

Kasey Kure writes his thoughts in response to an IMP problem.

Where's Speedy?

Speedy is the star runner for her country's track team. Among other things, she runs the last 400 meters of the 1600-meter relay race.

A sports analyst recently studied the film of a race in which she competed. The analyst came up with this formula to describe the distance Speedy had run at a given time in the race.

$$m(t) = 0.1t^2 + 3t$$

In this formula, $m(t)$ gives the number of meters Speedy had run after t seconds of the race, with both time and distance measured from the beginning of her 400-meter segment of the race. (This formula might not be very accurate, but you are to work on this activity as if it were completely correct.)

1. Use the formula for $m(t)$ to fill in several rows of this In-Out table to show how far Speedy had run at different times of the race.

t	$m(t)$

2. Use the table from Question 1 to make a graph that represents this situation. You may need to add more information to your table in order to obtain a graph that shows the entire time she is running.

3. Write an equation using the variable t that you could solve to get the answer to the question "How long does it take Speedy to run her first 200 meters?"

4. Graph the function $m(t) = 0.1t^2 + 3t$ on the graphing calculator and use your graph to get an approximate solution to your equation from Question 3.

Homework 27   A Mixed Bag

1. Find the numerical solution to each of these linear equations. Be sure to check your answers.

   a. $5a + 3 = 7a - 9$

   b. $4(t + 7) - 2(t - 3) = 8t + 11$

2. Solve each of these equations for the variable indicated in terms of the other variables.

   a. Solve for r in terms of u.

   $$8u + 5r - 14 = 0$$

   b. Solve for y in terms of a, b, c, and x.

   $$ax + by = c$$

   c. Solve for m in terms of n.

   $$3m^2 + 5n^2 = 21$$

To the Rescue

A helicopter is flying to drop a supply bundle to a group of firefighters who are behind the fire lines. At the moment when the helicopter crew makes the drop, the helicopter is hovering 400 feet above the ground.

The principles of physics that describe the behavior of falling objects state that when an object is falling freely, it goes faster and faster as it falls. In fact, these principles provide a specific formula describing the object's fall, which can be expressed this way:

Suppose that the object's height off the ground when it begins to fall, at time $t = 0$, is N feet, and use $h(t)$ to represent the object's height off the ground t seconds after being dropped. Then the function $h(t)$ is given by the equation $h(t) = N - 16t^2$.

So in the case of the falling supplies, the formula is $h(t) = 400 - 16t^2$, because the supply bundle is 400 feet off the ground when it starts to fall.

1. How many seconds will it take the bundle to reach the ground? (*Hint:* What is $h(t)$ when the bundle reaches the ground?)

2. Write an equation that you could use to find out how many seconds it takes until the supply bundle is 100 feet off the ground.

3. Use a graphing calculator to find an approximate solution to your equation from Question 2.

4. Explain how you could check your solution from Question 2 using the formula $h(t) = 400 - 16t^2$.

Homework 28   Swinging Pendulum

In Question 4 of *Memories of Yesteryear,* you read about a group of students doing experiments with pendulums. They expressed the period of a pendulum as a function of its length by the formula $P = 0.32\sqrt{L}$, where P is the time of one period (expressed in seconds) and L is the length of the pendulum (expressed in inches).

1. Use the students' formula to find the period for pendulums with each of these lengths.

   a. 4 inches

   b. 16 inches

   c. 50 inches

   d. 10 feet

2. Use your answers from Question 1 and other data that you obtain from the formula to sketch a graph of the function. Use scales for your axes that are appropriate for your answers to Question 1.

After they found their formula, the students decided to build a clock using a pendulum. They wanted the period of the pendulum to be exactly one second.

3. Write an equation that they could use to find the correct length for their pendulum.

4. Find a solution to your equation. (Give an approximate value if necessary.)

5. Explain in words how you could use a graph of the function to solve the equation.

Mystery Graph

The graph below shows the variable y as a function of x, but it doesn't give a formula for this function. Instead, the graph is labeled with the generic function equation, $y = f(x)$.

Answer these questions based on the graph. Give approximate answers if necessary and state any assumptions you make about any portion of the graph that isn't visible.

1. a. Find $f(4)$. That is, what number would you get for y if you substituted 4 for x?

    b. Find $f(0)$.

    c. Find $f(-1)$.

    d. Find $f(-4)$.

2. Find all solutions to the equation $f(x) = 0$. That is, find all the values of x for which y is 0.

3. Solve each of these equations, giving all possible solutions.

    a. $f(x) = 7$

    b. $f(x) = 1$

    c. $f(x) = -2$

    d. $f(x) = -5$

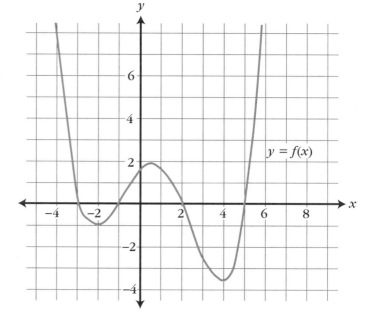

4. a. Find the maximum point for the part of the function between $x = -3$ and $x = 3$. That is, what point with an x-coordinate between -3 and 3 has the largest y-coordinate?

    b. Find the minimum point for the part of the function between $x = -3$ and $x = 3$.

5. Solve the inequality $f(x) > 0$. That is, find the values for x that give a positive value for y. Describe all possible answers.

Homework 29

Functioning in the Math World

Part I: Expressions, Graphs, Tables, and Situations

Algebraic expressions, graphs, and In-Out tables are three ways of representing the concept that mathematicians refer to using the word **function.** Mathematicians often blur the distinctions among these three representations, referring to them all as "the function."

Functions also are often connected to real-life situations. In this assignment, you will look at how these four ideas—expressions, graphs, tables, and situations—are related to one another. (Sometimes people use the phrase *rule of four* to refer to these four ways of thinking about functions.)

1. The area of a square is determined by the length of any of its sides. For instance, if the length of a side is 7 inches, then the area is 49 square inches. Therefore, we can say that the area is *a function of* this length.

   a. Make an In-Out table to go with this situation and fill in several rows for this table. (The values 7 and 49 would make up one row of your table.)

Continued on next page

b. Express the relationship between area and length in terms of an equation, explaining any variables you use.

c. Make a graph of your equation.

2. The equation $y = 3x + 1$ can be used to define a function.

   a. Make an In-Out table to go with this equation and fill in several rows for this table.

   b. Sketch the graph of the equation.

   c. Create a situation for which this equation might be appropriate. Explain the role of the variables x and y in your situation.

Part II: Another Mystery Graph

3. Study the graph of the function h shown below and then answer the questions. (You should consider only the part of the function shown in this graph.)

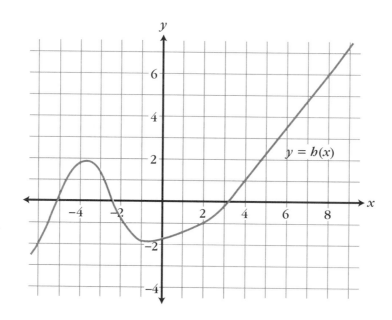

$y = h(x)$

a. Estimate the value of $h(5)$.

b. Estimate the y-intercept of the function h.

Continued on next page

   c. Estimate the x-intercepts of the function h.

   d. Estimate all solutions to the equation $h(x) = -1$.

Part III: Making Graphs That Fit Conditions

In these problems, you are asked to sketch graphs that fit certain conditions. Many graphs will work, but you need to create only one of them. *Note:* Most graphs are infinite, so the graph you actually draw will probably be only part of the total graph.

4. Sketch the graph for a function f that satisfies both of these conditions.

    • The function f has exactly three x-intercepts.

    • $f(2) = 5$

5. Sketch the graph for a function k that satisfies all of these conditions.

    • The function k has no x-intercepts.

    • $k(-1) = 2$

    • $k(3) = 1$

    • $k(5) = 6$

The Graphing Calculator Solver

In *Where's Speedy?* the expression $0.1t^2 + 3t$ told you how far Speedy would run in the first t seconds. The expression was used to define the function $m(t)$.

You then wrote and solved equations with this expression to answer questions about Speedy. For example, you solved the equation $0.1t^2 + 3t = 200$ to find out how long it would take Speedy to run the first 200 meters of her part of the race. You may have used the graph of the function $m(t)$ to solve such equations.

Continued on next page

Equations, Functions, and Graphs

You can use this method to solve equations even when the equation doesn't come from a real-life situation. For example, even if you saw the equation $0.1t^2 + 3t = 200$ out of context, you could still enter the expression $0.1X^2 + 3X$ into a graphing calculator to define a function and get a graph. You could then solve the equation (approximately) by using the trace feature to find the values of X that make Y equal to 200. (In addition to the solution you found earlier, there is also a negative solution for X, which you would ignore if X represented time.)

A Graph Is Like an Answer Key

There's nothing magical about the expression $0.1t^2 + 3t$. Any meaningful expression that can be entered into a graphing calculator can be used to define a function. Once you've entered the expression, the graph of the function becomes an answer key for an entire family of equations involving that expression. For example, the graph of Speedy's function doesn't just help you solve the equation $0.1t^2 + 3t = 200$. It also helps you solve $0.1t^2 + 3t = 100$, $0.1t^2 + 3t = 63$, or any similar equation.

Your Task

Your task in this activity is to use the graphing calculator to solve the equations given below. Give your answers to the nearest tenth.

Note: For simplicity, these equations have been chosen so that their solutions all lie between $x = -5$ and $x = 5$.

1. $2x^2 + 5x + 7 = 20$

2. $x^3 + 4x^2 - 5x + 1 = 12$

3. $x^4 - x^3 + 3x^2 + 5x = 6$

4. $x^3 + 4x = 2x^2 + 7x - 1$ (*Hint:* Use the expressions on each side of the equation to define two different functions. Then think of the original equation as asking for the value of x that gives the same function value for both functions.)

Homework 30   A Solving Sampler

You have used several ideas and methods for solving equations as part of this unit.

- Guess and check

- The mystery-bags model

- "Unscrambling" equations (equivalent equations)

- Graphing

In this activity, you will examine each of these methods as part of the preparation for your *Solve It!* portfolio.

1. Begin with the guess-and-check method.

   a. Summarize how the method works.

   b. Select an activity from the unit in which that method played an important role and attach that activity.

   c. Make up an equation for which you would use that method.

2. Do parts a, b, and c of Question 1 for the mystery-bags model.

3. Do parts a, b, and c of Question 1 for the equivalent-equations method.

4. Do parts a, b, and c of Question 1 for the graphing method.

"Solve It!" Portfolio

Now that *Solve It!* is completed, it is time to put together your portfolio for the unit. This activity has three parts.

- Writing a cover letter summarizing the unit

- Choosing papers to include from your work in this unit

- Comparing this unit to Year 1 IMP units and to traditional algebra

Cover Letter for "Solve It!"

Look back over *Solve It!* and describe the main mathematical ideas of the unit. This description should give an overview of how the key ideas were developed. In compiling your portfolio, you will be selecting some activities that you think were important in developing the key ideas of this unit. Your cover letter should include an explanation of why you selected particular items.

Continued on next page

Papers from "Solve It!"

Your portfolio for *Solve It!* should contain these items.

- *Homework 30: A Solving Sampler*
  Include both what you wrote about the different methods for solving equations and the sample activities you chose.

- *Get It Straight*
  Include your write-up of your work on this activity.

- *Homework 24: A Distributive Summary*

- A Problem of the Week
  Select one of the three POWs you completed during this unit (*A Digital Proof* or *Tying the Knots* or *Divisor Counting*).

- Other high-quality work
  Select one or two other pieces of work that represent your best efforts. (These can be any work from the unit—Problem of the Week, homework, classwork, presentation, and so on.)

"Solve It!" and Algebra

This unit is more traditional than most of the IMP units. For example, it doesn't have a central problem, and it involves manipulating algebra symbols. Discuss your reaction to this type of unit. You might comment on these issues.

- How did you like this unit compared to Year 1 units with a central problem?

- Are you glad you did a unit emphasizing these traditional skills? Why or why not?

- How does the material in this unit compare with your idea of what algebra is?

Appendix

Supplemental Problems

As in Year 1, the supplemental problems for each unit pursue some of the themes and ideas that are important in that unit. Some of the supplemental problems in ***Solve It!*** continue the theme of looking back at ideas from Year 1. Others pursue ideas about equivalent expressions or follow up on ideas from the POWs. Here are some examples.

- *What to Expect* and *Carlos and Betty* give you more opportunities to work with the concept of expected value from the Year 1 unit *The Game of Pig*.

- *Same Expectations* and *Preserve the Distributive Property* give you a chance to extend your understanding of the distributive property and how it is used.

- *Ten Missing Digits* and *The Locker Problem* continue themes from *POW 1: A Digital Proof* and *POW 3: Divisor Counting*.

What to Expect?

One of the problems from *Memories of Yesteryear* involved Al and Betty and the spinner shown below. This problem poses some more questions about that spinner.

1. a. If Al wins 4 points when the spinner lands on the gray area, what is his expected gain or loss per spin in the long run?

   b. If Al wins 10 points when the spinner lands on gray, what is his expected gain or loss per spin in the long run?

2. Al likes playing spinner games. He's willing to lose an average of $\frac{1}{4}$ point per spin in order to keep playing. Assume that Betty still wins 2 points when the spinner lands on white. What payoff should Al be willing to take each time the spinner lands on gray so that his expected loss is $\frac{1}{4}$ point per spin?

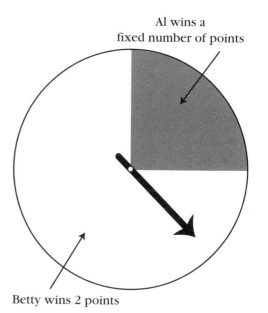

Al wins a fixed number of points

Betty wins 2 points

3. Make an In-Out table, based on the spinner shown above, in which the *In* is the amount Al wins when the spinner lands on gray and the *Out* is Al's average gain or loss per spin for that payoff. (Betty always gets 2 points when she wins.)

4. Find a rule for your In-Out table.

Carlos and Betty

Carlos also likes spinner games. He has a spinner like the one at the right, in which Betty wins when the spinner lands in the white area ($\frac{2}{3}$ of the time). She gets 2 points from Carlos every time she wins.

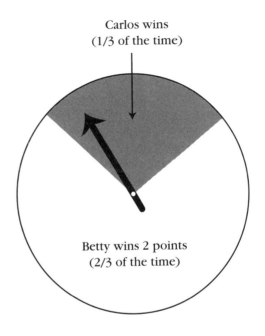

Carlos wins
(1/3 of the time)

Betty wins 2 points
(2/3 of the time)

1. How many points should Carlos win when the spinner lands in the gray area in order for the game to be fair? Explain how you got your answer.

2. Betty thinks it's fun to play spinner games. In fact, she is willing to lose points in the long run in order to keep Carlos interested in playing.

   How many points should she give him for the spins he wins if she wants his average gain in the long run to be

   a. $\frac{1}{10}$ point per spin?

   b. $\frac{1}{2}$ point per spin?

   Explain how you got your answers.

Hint on both Question 1 and Question 2: Experiment with various payoff amounts, find Carlos' expected value for each, and make an In-Out chart.

Ten Missing Digits

In *Is It a Digit?* you had to fill in five empty boxes, labeled 0 through 4, in a way that satisfied certain conditions. In this problem, you have to solve a harder version of that problem. Specifically, consider the ten boxes below:

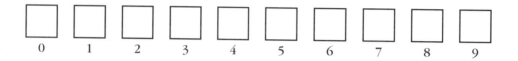

0   1   2   3   4   5   6   7   8   9

The rules are that you must put a digit from 0 to 9 in each of the boxes so that these conditions hold.

- The digit you put in the box labeled "0" must be the same as the number of 0's you use.

- The digit you put in the box labeled "1" must be the same as the number of 1's you use.

- The digit you put in the box labeled "2" must be the same as the number of 2's you use, and so on.

As in *Is It a Digit?* you are allowed to use the same digit more than once.

There may be more than one solution to this problem, so part of your task is to show that you have all the possible answers.

Same Expectations

You may have noticed in your work with expected value in *The Game of Pig* that it didn't matter how many games or how many spins you used as "the long run." Here's your chance to see why.

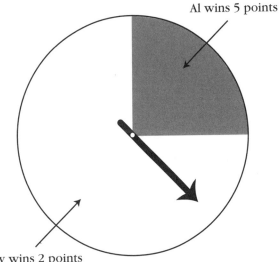

Al wins 5 points

The spinner shown here is the same as in Question 3 of *Memories of Yesteryear,* except that now it shows Al winning 5 points each time the spinner lands on gray. As before, Betty wins 2 points each time the spinner lands on white.

Betty wins 2 points

1. Suppose Al and Betty do a total of 100 spins. Assume that the results follow the probabilities perfectly and find Betty's average gain per spin. Your expression should show your reasoning in terms of the 100 spins.

2. Repeat Question 1 but use 1000 spins this time.

3. Repeat Question 1 but this time use the variable N for the number of spins. Use a little algebra to prove that if the results follow the probabilities perfectly, then Betty's average gain per spin is the same no matter how many spins there are.

Preserve the Distributive Property

Some of the rules for multiplication with integers make intuitive sense, but others can be confusing. For example, the fact that $3(-2) = -6$ can be explained in terms of repeated addition:

$$3(-2) = -2 + (-2) + (-2)$$

The fact that $-2 + (-2) + (-2) = -6$ also seems reasonable, so we have $3(-2) = -6$.

It also seems intuitively reasonable to most people that $0(-2) = 0$. But many people have a hard time understanding why the product of two negative numbers should be positive. It turns out that the distributive property can provide an explanation for this fact.

Your first task in this activity is to use the expression $(-3 + 3)(-2)$ to show that $(-3)(-2) = 6$. The key idea is to evaluate $(-3 + 3)(-2)$ in two different ways, using the distributive property in one of the ways. Then generalize this example to explain why the product of any two negative numbers must be positive. You may assume that the product of a positive number and a negative number is negative.

The Locker Problem

Louise is walking through the hallway of her school past the row of lockers on the first day of school. The lockers are numbered from 1 to 100. When Louise gets to the lockers, they are all open. Absentmindedly, Louise closes all the even-numbered lockers—the multiples of 2—as she walks by.

A few minutes later, Jeremy comes by. He decides to touch only those lockers whose numbers are multiples of 3. If one of these lockers is open when he goes by, he closes it, and if it's closed, he opens it. (For example, Louise left locker 3 open, so Jeremy closes it. Louise closed locker 6, so Jeremy opens it, and so on.)

Then another student comes by, and this student changes the doors on all the lockers whose numbers are multiples of 4. Then another student changes the doors on lockers whose numbers are multiples of 5, and so on, until finally a student comes by who changes only locker 100.

The question is,

Which lockers are open at the end of the process?

You should not only determine which lockers end up open but also find an explanation for the result. Once you're done, explain which lockers would end up open if the locker numbers went up to 1000. (Assume that the last student changes only locker 1000.)

Who's Got an Equivalent?

For each of the expressions below:

- Find an expression without parentheses that is equivalent to the given one.

- Explain why the two expressions are equivalent. (Thinking about the hot-and-cold-cube model may help.)

1. $12 - (a + 7)$

2. $26 - (12 - 3t)$

3. $41 - 2(b + 1)$

Make It Simple

The task of removing parentheses from an expression being subtracted is a tricky one, and not easy to explain. When the expression in parentheses itself involves subtraction (as in Question 2 of *Who's Got an Equivalent?*), it's even harder.

1. Describe and explain the steps involved in simplifying these expressions.

    a. $20 - 5(x + 3)$

    b. $20 - 5(x - 3)$

2. The next expression can be simplified all the way to $4x + 7$. Show the process of simplifying it to that point.

$$6(3x + 4) - 4(x - 2) - 5(2x + 5)$$

Linear in a Variable

Much of your work in *Solve It!* has involved linear equations and linear expressions. Some of the ideas for working with linear equations can be applied to equations that are not linear. An important case involves equations and expressions that include more than one variable but that are linear "in a particular variable."

For example, consider the expression $4u + tu + 9$. This expression is not linear, because it involves the product of two variables, t and u. But if t were replaced by a specific number, the expression would become linear. For instance, substituting 3 for t gives $4u + 3u + 9$, which is equivalent to the linear expression $7u + 9$.

The expression $4u + tu + 9$ is called **linear in u,** because replacing the other variable by a number gives a linear expression. You can use the distributive property to see that this expression is equivalent to $(4 + t)u + 9$. You can think of the sum $4 + t$ as the coefficient of u.

1. Solve the equation $4u + tu + 9 = 6t - 4$ for u in terms of t.

2. Solve each of the equations below for the variable indicated. In each case, the equation is linear in that variable, even if the equation as a whole is not linear.

   a. Solve for c in terms of a.

   $$ac + 3c = 5a - (c + 7)$$

   b. Solve for w in terms of u and v.

   $$4uw + v = 3w + v^2$$

The Shadow Equation Revisited

Do you remember this picture from *Shadows* in Year 1? The small triangle and the big triangle in this diagram are similar, so the variables *S, D, H,* and *L* satisfy the equation

$$\frac{S}{S+D} = \frac{H}{L}$$

(Remember that *S* + *D* is the length of the horizontal side of the big triangle.)

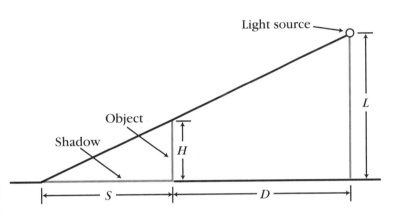

Your goal in *Shadows* was to express *S* directly as a function of *L, H,* and *D*. One way to accomplish this is to add a line segment to the diagram that creates another triangle similar to the original two. This gives another equation that is easier to use in solving for *S*.

1. Your first task in this activity is to use algebra instead of a new diagram to accomplish the *Shadows* goal.

   a. Find an equation equivalent to $\frac{S}{S+D} = \frac{H}{L}$ that expresses *S* in terms of *L, H,* and *D*. In other words, your equation should begin "*S* = " and have an expression involving the other three variables on the right side.
   (*Hint:* First find an equivalent equation that has no fractions in it, and then use the distributive property and factoring.)

   b. In *Lamppost Shadows,* Nelson was standing 20 feet from a 25-foot lamppost. Nelson is 6 feet tall. Use the equation you got in Question 1a to find the length of his shadow.

2. Algebra can be used to solve for other variables as well.

   a. Find an equation equivalent to $\frac{S}{S+D} = \frac{H}{L}$ that expresses *D* in terms of *L, H,* and *S.*

   b. Use your equation from Question 2a to find out where Nelson should stand in order to cast a 50-foot shadow.

A Function—Not!

You have occasionally used In-Out tables in contexts in which these tables did not represent functions. For example, in *The Overland Trail,* a table showed the number of people in the group in one column and the amount used of a supply item in another. This relationship wasn't a function because groups of the same size might have used different amounts of the item.

The distinction between a function and an arbitrary set of pairs is sometimes important and might be stated like this:

> The term *function* is only applicable when the *Out* is completely determined by the *In*. In other words, for an In-Out table to represent a function, there can only be one value for the *Out* for any particular choice of the *In*.

The Vertical-Line Test

One way to identify which graphs are graphs of functions is to apply the **vertical-line test:**

> For a graph to represent a function, no vertical line can go through more than one of its points.

Note: The definition of the term *function* permits many *In* numbers to have the same *Out,* so there is no "horizontal-line test" required for functions.

1. Identify which of these graphs are graphs of functions, and explain your decisions.

   a.

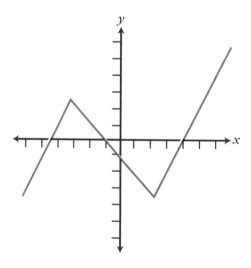

Continued on next page

b.

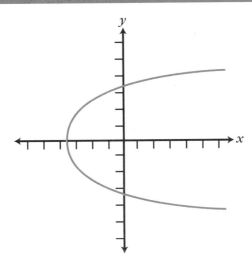

c.

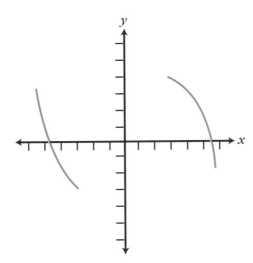

2. Explain why the vertical-line test tells you if a graph represents a function or not.

Photographic Credits

Interior Photography

3 Lincoln High School, Lori Green; **17** Santa Cruz High School, Kevin Drinkard, Lynne Alper; **36** Foothill High School, Cheryl Dozier; **65** Brookline High School, Priscilla Burbank-Schmitt, Carla Oblas; **70** Lumina Designworks, Terry Lockman; **75** Hillary Turner; **77** Fresno High School, Dave Calhoun

Cover Photography and Cover Illustration

Background © Tony Stone Worldwide **Top left to bottom right** From *Alice in Wonderland* by Lewis Carroll; Hillary Turner; Hillary Turner; © Image Bank

Front Cover Students

Colin Bjorklund, Liana Steinmetz, Sita Davis, Thea Singleton, Jenée Desmond, Jennifer Lynn Anker, Lidia Murillo, Keenzia Budd, Noel Sanchez, Seogwon Lee, Kolin Bonet (photographed by Hillary Turner)